It is Fun

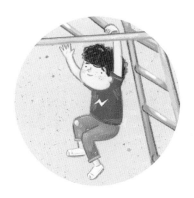

Kasia Reay

Illustrated by Lisa Molloy

Schofield & Sims

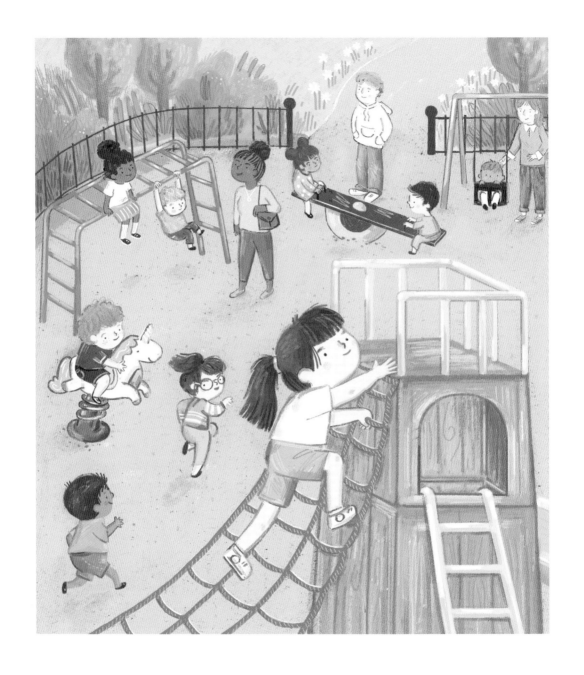

It is fun to go up...

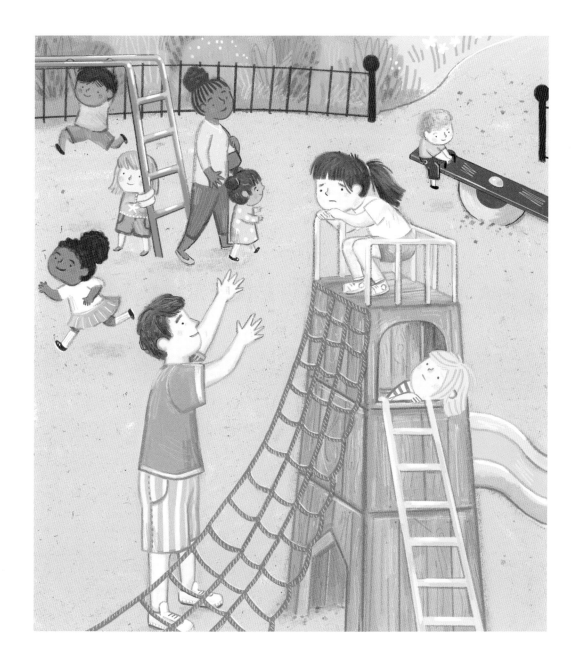

but is it fun to get o<u>ff</u>?

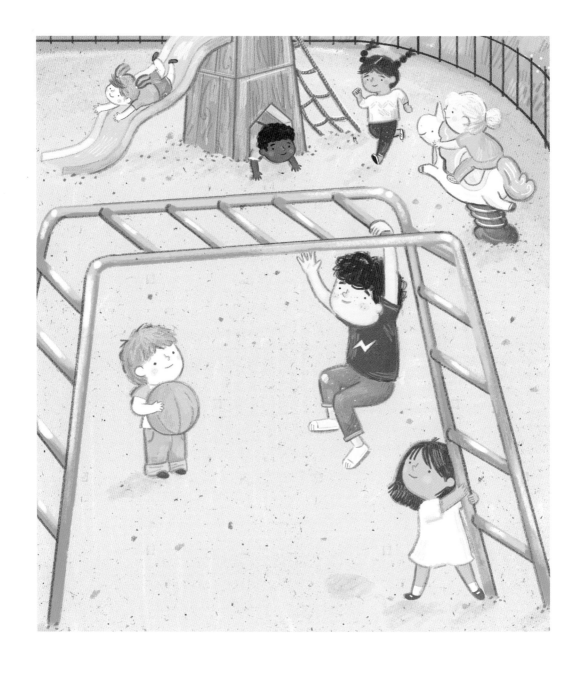

It is fun to get on...

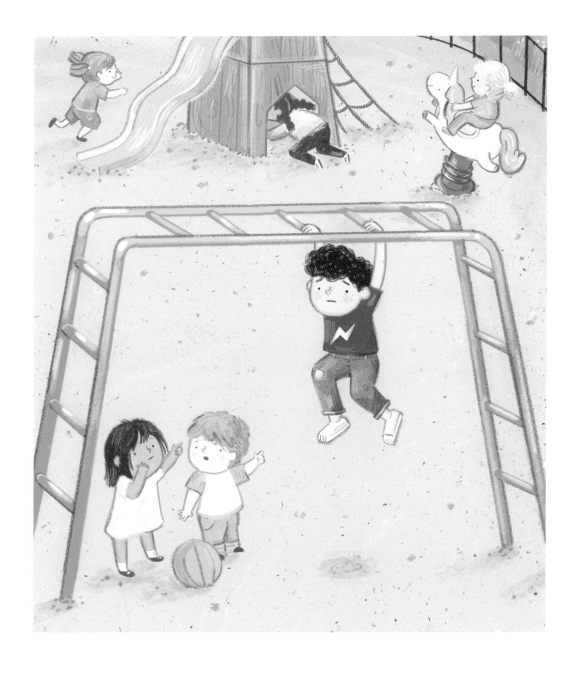

but is it fun to get o<u>ff</u>?

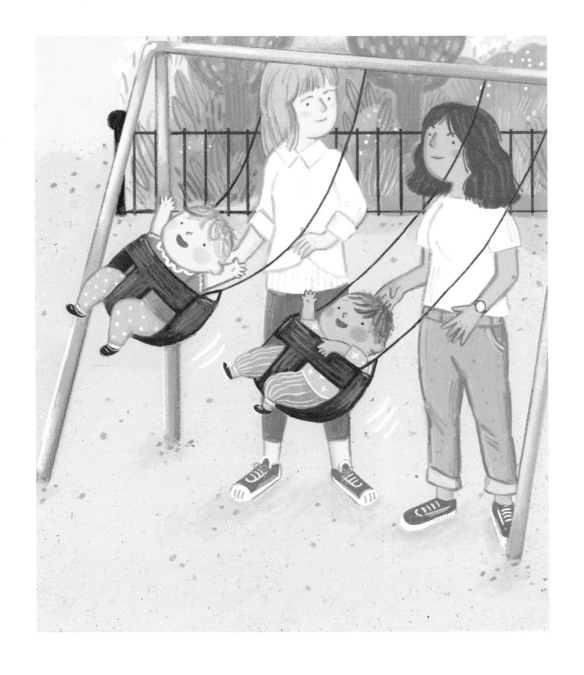

It is fun to go up.

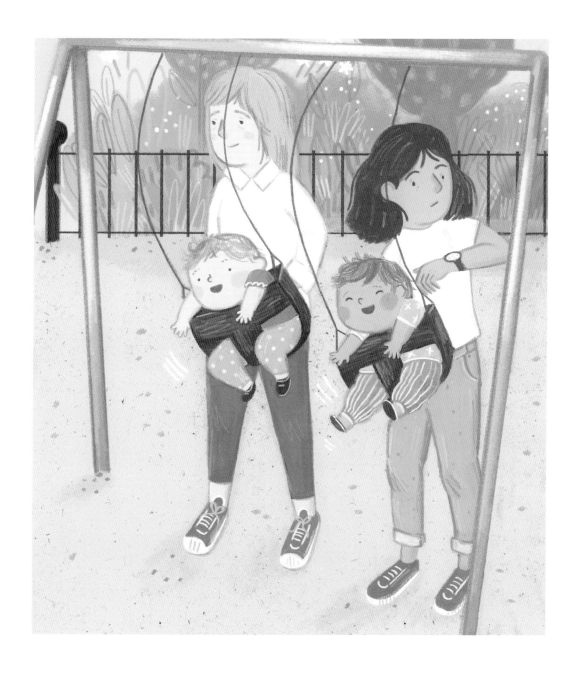

It is fun to go ba<u>ck</u>.

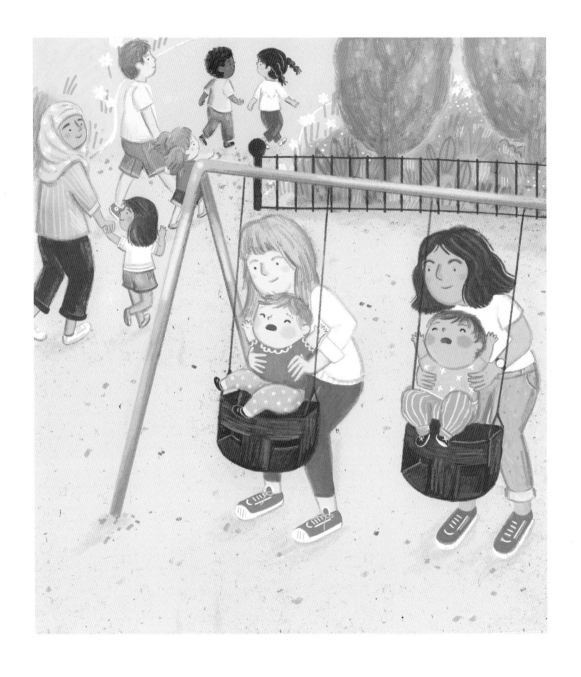

It is not fun to get off!